bendon®

D1550380

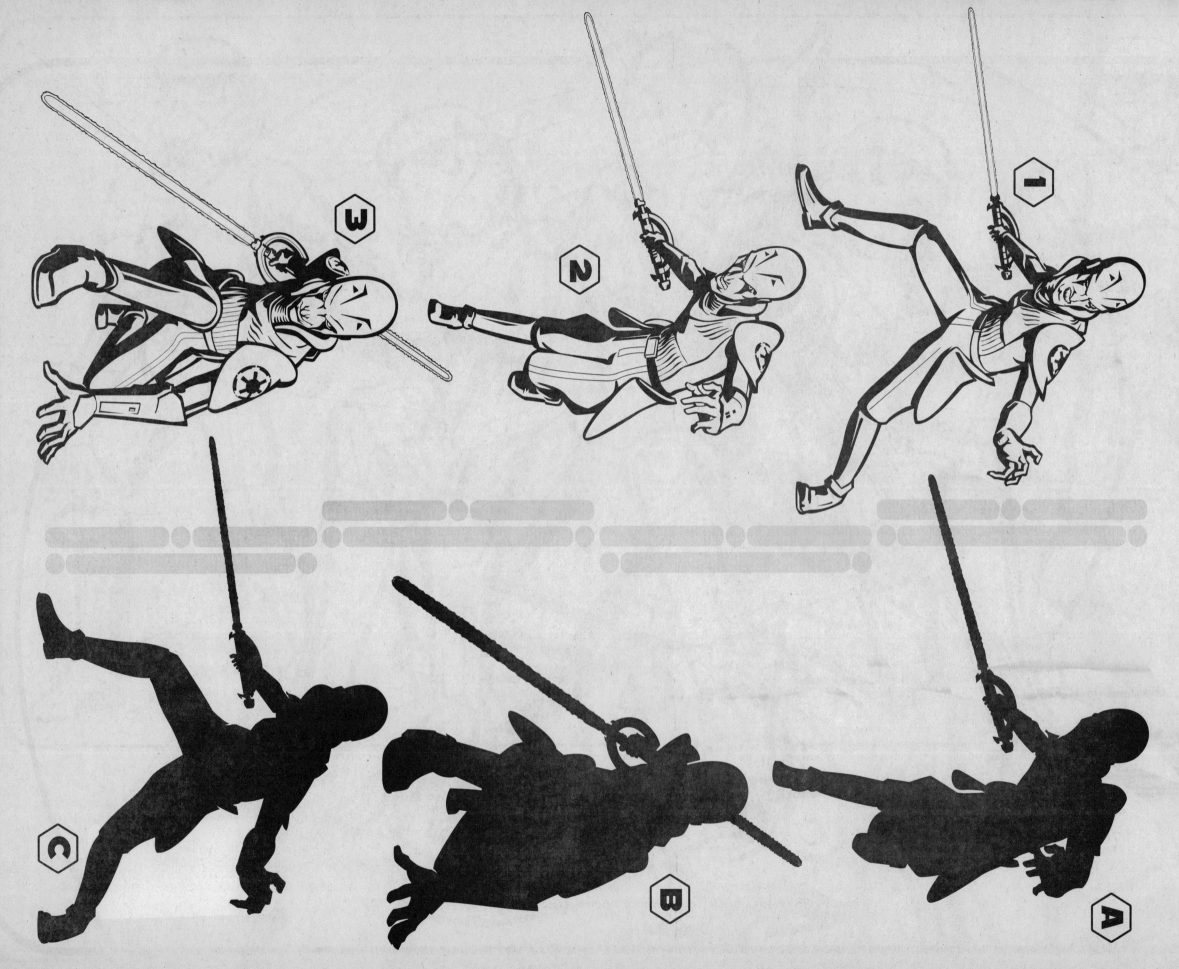

IMPERIAL SHADOWS

Draw lines to match each Inquisitor with his correct shadow.

CHOPPED IN HALF

Chopper has been put together from many parts. Draw the other half of the Rebels' droid.

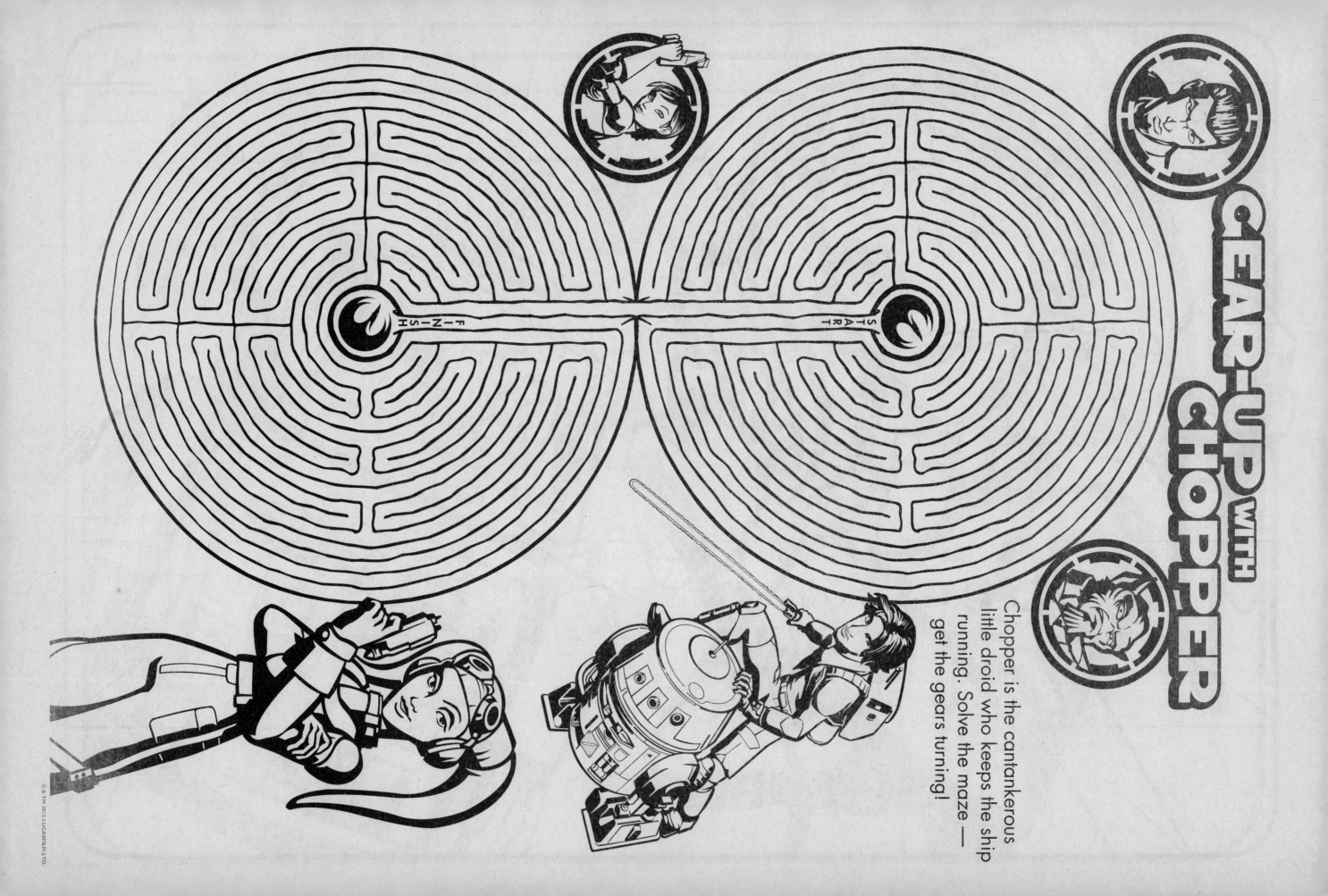

GEAR-UP WITH CHOPPER

START

FINISH

Chopper is the cantankerous little droid who keeps the ship running. Solve the maze — get the gears turning!

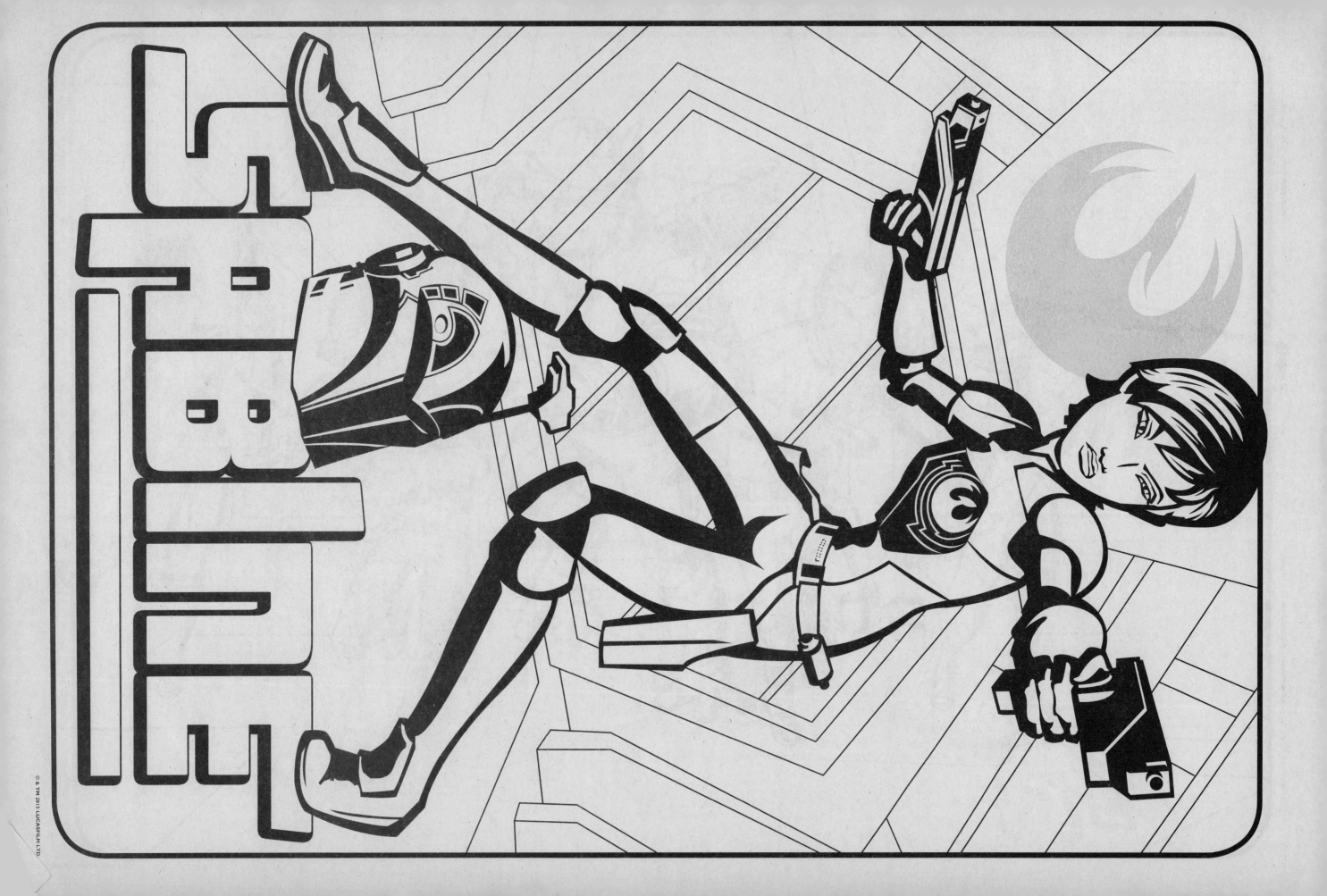

TIE FIGHTERS

The swift, maneuverable Twin Ion Engine fighters enforce the Imperial rule of the Galactic Empire. Draw the other half of this TIE fighter.

PHANTOM

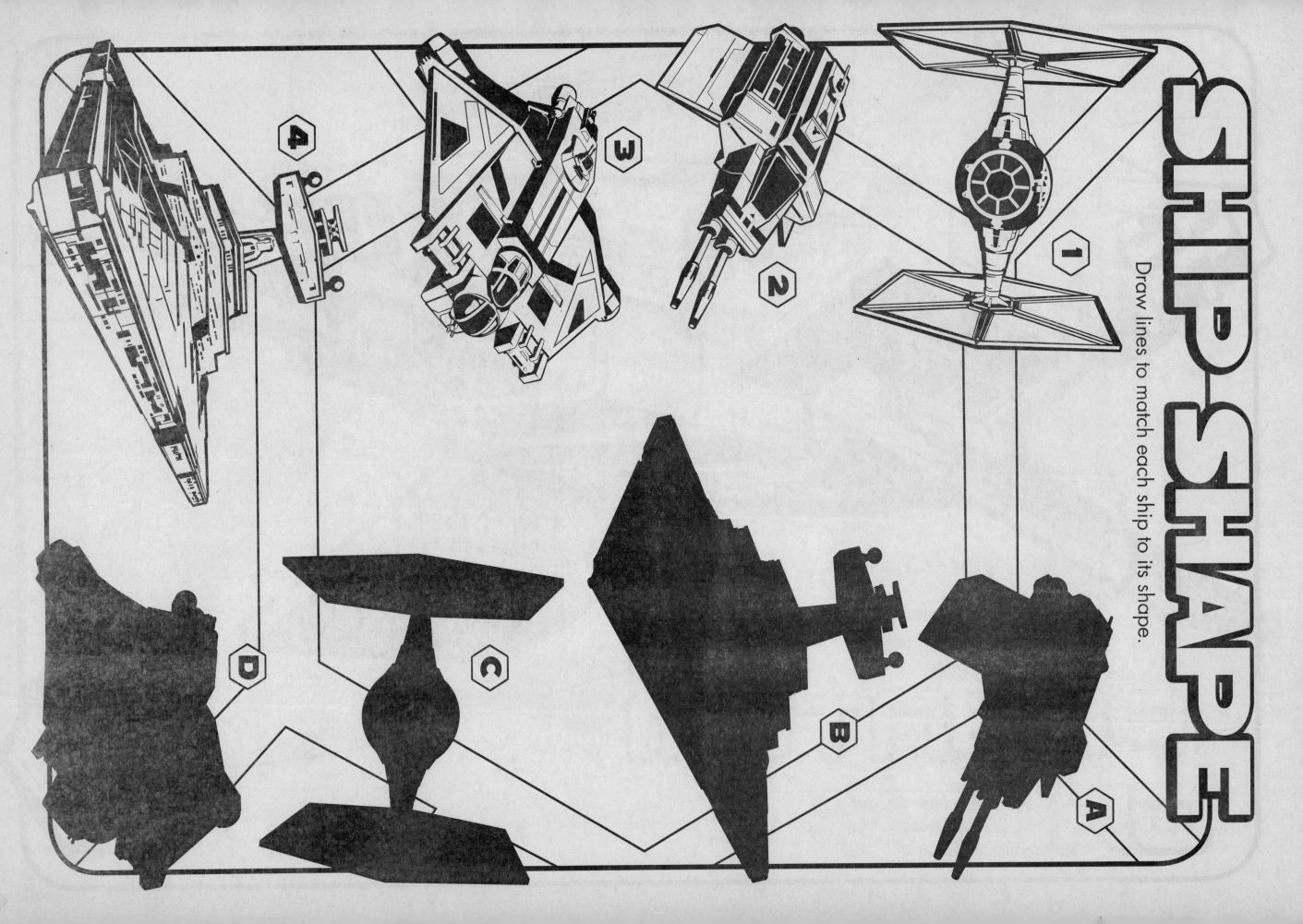

SHIP-SHAPE

Draw lines to match each ship to its shape.

GHOST

IMPERIAL SHADOWS

Draw lines to match each stormtrooper with its shadow.

DRAW!

Imperial stormtroopers have been deployed.
Draw the other half of the stormtrooper.

IMPERIAL
RULE THE GALAXY
CRUSH THE REBELLION
FORCES